HONEYBEES THAT BUILD PERFECT COMBS

HARUN YAHYA

GOODWORD BOOKS
1, Nizamuddin West Market, New Delhi 110 013
Tel. 435 5454, 435 1128, 435 6666 • Fax 435 7333, 435 7980
E-mail: info@goodwordbooks.com • Website: www.goodwordforkids.com

First published 2002
© Goodword Books 2002

Printed in India

You all know about honeybees. Many of you have probably seen them in cartoons on TV, or even in real life, buzzing around. But I bet there are still many things you do not know about them...

Not long ago, mom and dad and I went to the woods to go jogging. I had a great time there. But what pleased me most was a new friend I made there while we were having a rest. It was quite tiny, but it meant a lot to me. I will never forget this little friend of mine.

You are probably wondering who it was, aren't you? Well, it was a lovely honeybee. It came up to me and flew around for a while. At first, I was afraid of being stung because it came very close... I screamed: "Don't! Please don't sting me. I don't want to be hurt!" And just then, something very strange happened, for the honeybee started talking to me.

The Honeybee: I don't want to sting you. I just want to be friends with you.

Omar: Really? I am very pleased to hear it!

The Honeybee: Let me introduce myself. I am a worker bee. I live in the trunk of that tree, together with thousands of my friends.

Omar: Wow! You have so many friends!... How do you and your friends spend your days?

The Honeybee: We clean our hive, collect food and carry it to the hive, produce royal jelly, keep the hive warm and guard it...

7

8

All the honeybees in the hive do different jobs. Some collect food while others clean the hive or produce honey.

Omar: Don't you get tired doing all that?

The Honeybee: No. We worker bees split the jobs in the hive up amongst ourselves. That is why we never get tired. For example, these days I am building combs to store honey...

Omar: There is one thing I have always wondered about bees; how are you born?

The Honeybee: You have probably heard that there is a queen in every honeybee colony. The queen bee is the biggest of all the female bees. She lays eggs at certain times. But we do not hatch from the eggs straight away. What hatch from these eggs are white grubs, called larvae, with no eyes, wings or legs, and which do not look like us at all. For a while, they remain wrapped in a cocoon. In the meantime, they are fully fed and then emerge from the cocoon looking exactly like me.

Omar: That is amazing! I am still curious about one more thing though! Being so crowded, isn't there any disorder in your hive?

The Honeybee: Never. On the contrary, it's really well ordered. Thousands of bees live together in great harmony while we do all our jobs.

Omar: That is really very interesting! I still can't understand how you can manage to keep order although there are so many of you! My dad is the manager of our building, and he really has a hard time keeping order there. But you say you have no such problem!

The eggs laid by the queen bee in the cells first look like the grubs in the picture below. These larvae grow over time, develop and take the shape of a bee. The big picture below shows the worker bees that have gathered around the queen.

The Honeybee: You are right to be surprised. I know that scientists are amazed by this too, and look for answers to the questions of how order is kept, how each honeybee knows what its job is supposed to be, and how such a large number of bees can act together so well! I can tell you the answer quite quickly: We all have certain tasks; we work hard and carry them out as best as we can and try not to disturb the order in the hive.

While listening to the worker bee in wonder, I heard my mom calling, "Omar! Omar! Where are you?" It was time for me to leave.

Omar: My mom is calling me. I think I have to go now. I am so pleased to meet you. Thanks for everything you told me!

The Honeybee: I also enjoyed your company. Maybe, we can meet again! How about meeting here again next week? If you like, I can take you to our hive and show you the combs.

Omar: That would be great! But only if my parents agree to come here again, of course.

The Honeybee: O.K., hope to see you next week!

Honeybees feeding one another. (next) Bees fanning the hive with their wings. (below)

Worker bees feeding the larvae in the cells (next). Bees surrounding the trunk of a tree. (above)

As soon as I got home, I took out the encyclopaedia of animals my dad had given me as a birthday present. I quickly turned the pages and found the section on honeybees. The first thing that struck my eye was a little picture of a honeybee. I felt that I was already missing my little friend...

I read the book with wonder. I was so amazed by the things I read that I did not notice how much time had passed. My mom wondered what I was doing in my room for so long and came to look for me. I excitedly started to tell her all about bees.

Omar: Mom, did you know that honeybees are really fascinating? For instance, let me tell you the last thing I read here; you have probably heard that female

honeybees do the cleaning in the cells. They throw out all the particles left behind by the bees hatching from their cocoons, bees that have died in the hive and many other things that don't belong in the hive. Do you know what they do when they come across something too big for them to carry out of the hive? They embalm it with a material called "propolis" to prevent it from producing bacteria and harming the health of the other bees in the hive. It is hard to believe, but propolis is an anti-bacterial material, that is, it stops bacteria growing... Do you know where they find this substance, mom? How do these tiny beings know so much about chemistry? That is as far as I have read. Maybe I can tell you how they make this substance later.

(Left) The worker bees are responsible for carrying out all sorts of organisms and dead larvae that can threaten the security and health of the hive.

(Right) Worker bees pushing a stranger out of the hive.

Mother: Bees are tiny yet extremely intelligent animals... However, it would be wrong to think that this intelligence belongs to them. There is a Creator Who teaches them everything they do. When I was your age, I also read a book about honeybees which impressed me very much, just like you. If you like, you can keep on reading. I would love to hear more about honeybees whenever you want to share what you've learnt with me.

My mom went out of the room to prepare supper. That question was still on my mind; where do honeybees find the material called "propolis" and where do they learn how to use it? I kept on reading with wonder.

The book also mentioned how honeybees produce propolis. They first collect a material called resin from the sticky buds of some trees with the help of their lower jaws. They then produce propolis by adding their saliva to the resin, and carry it to the hive in the special sacs on their feet.

Honeybees wrap up anything they cannot carry out of the hive in this substance they store in the sacs on their feet. This way, that material cannot house any bacteria and becomes harmless. This is an operation similar to mummifying.

But who taught honeybees to do this? How do they know that a dead creature or waste material could harm the bees in the hive? Even I have only just learned this now. This is not something an insect could know! I was growing more and more curious. Could it be that honeybees were as conscious as human beings?

I could not help but read more. I thought to myself: "Now I understand that up until now I knew nothing about bees!" I still had many questions in my mind which I could not answer. But I was sure that sooner or later I would find the answers.

Honeybees collecting sticky tree buds to produce propolis.

The book also told how bees make honey. I had heard that honeybees make honey, but I had no idea how they built the honeycombs. Even the method they use while building the combs is a great miracle by itself!

The honeycomb cells are in the form of hexagons, six-sided figures. Honeybees start building the comb from the upper side of the hive. Starting from several points, they build two or three separate rows downward. I was completely confused; How could a honeycomb be so regular when it was built beginning from different points? Moreover, there is no sign of the junction points between the honeycomb cells.

I had seen mom knitting many times. She always started from one point. I wondered how the sweaters would look if she started from three separate points... Most probably, they would not look so good! So, honeybees must be animals which make very fine calculations...

I took a sheet of paper and a pencil. Starting from different corners, I started to draw hexagons (six-sided figures). I tried to join these hexagons up in the middle of the paper. I tried to do this without the help of any tools like rulers and set squares and without making any calculations.

But soon I realised that this was an impossible operation. So how can honeybees do this? How can they make hexagonal cells so perfectly?

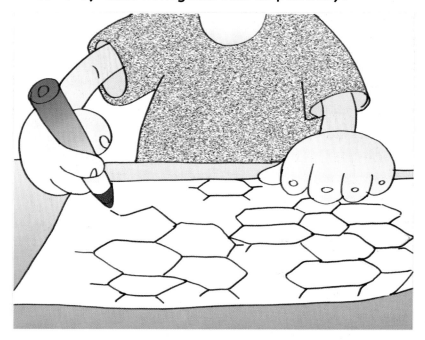

Omar tries to draw hexagons as neatly as the honeybees. But without the help of certain tools like rulers and set squares, he is not as successful as the bees. You can also try this for yourself.

No junction points appear on the honeycombs constructed by honeybees. The honeycomb is a uniform body, as if it were made by only one person. This is really amazing because bees start to build the cells which will form the honeycomb from different points.

21

Another point which drew my attention is that each bee that later joins the construction of the honeycomb immediately understands the stage things are at and takes charge of the job. As bees continue building cells from different corners, a totally different bee joining the team starts building from an entirely different angle. While such a process would normally cause great disorder, the bees build up a perfect structure.

I also read the section about bees' technique of making honey. I was very surprised and excited to read about this extraordinary process. The book said that the essence of honey is the nectar that bees collect from flowers and fruit buds. After collecting this nectar from flowers, bees turn it into honey.

There was one more important subject in the book: it takes a lot of hard work to produce honey. For instance, just to collect half a kilogram of nectar, 900 bees have to work for a full day. Other figures in the book were even more surprising: to produce 450 grams of pure honey, 17 thousand bees have to visit

Bees collect the essence of honey
from flowers and fruit buds.

24

10 million flowers. This is really tough work for them. Despite this, however, bees work very hard and produce much more honey than they need. Moreover, they do not use up much of the honey themselves, but offer it to us, human beings.

This was so puzzling. With their tiny bodies only a couple of centimetres long, bees were performing awesome tasks. What was the source of this consciousness, skill and power? How did they come to possess wisdom, consciousness and know so much about chemistry and mathematics? Why do they work so hard to produce honey?

I took my book and went to my dad. I told him everything I had learned, and asked him how bees could accomplish all these things. Smiling, dad patted my head and said:

"You are right. We see great wisdom and art in the lives of bees. But are they only in bees? Actually, there is perfect order in all animals and what is more, in every part of the universe! But first let me read you a verse from the Qur'an about bees to answer your questions. Listen carefully!"

Your Lord inspired the bees: Make hives in the mountains and in the trees and in men's habitations.

Then feed on all the fruits and walk in the ways of your Lord. There comes forth from within it a syrup of many colours, in which there is healing for men; most surely there is a sign in this for a people who reflect. (Surat an-Nahl: 68-69)

Omar: Now I get it better, dad. God 'inspires' the bees to behave in this amazing way. God is very compassionate to us and He inspires the bees to produce honey which contains healing properties for us. It is very exciting to learn about God's favours.

Father: If you examine ants or mosquitoes, camels, birds, fish, flowers, trees, stars, oceans, in short, anything on the Earth, you will feel the same wonder in the face of the perfection you see in them. All these show that every part of the universe is ruled by a great art. This is the artistry of God, Who created you and me and your mother, honeybees, parrots, rabbits, squirrels, planets, the space, the sun, in other words everything in the universe. God is the Lord of everything.

Everything takes place by His permission and by His Will. He is the Creator of the honeybees. Everything they do is with His permission. The wisdom we see in these animals is a reflection of God's endless wisdom. If you look at everything around you from this point of view, you will immediately notice the miracles you are surrounded by!

My father was right. There is no doubt that the wisdom we observe in everything surrounding us has an all-powerful Lord. I thought to myself, "God is the All-Powerful, the All-Wise, the Creator of everything." I had finally found all the answers to the questions that had been bothering me. Honeybees do not own the wisdom they display! It is impossible for them to possess such wisdom! They act by the inspiration of God, their Creator, and thus display a superior wisdom that astonishes us.

I spent the entire week telling everyone I met, my mom, dad, my cousins and friends, about honeybees. At the weekend, I asked my father to go to the woods again.

Omar: Daddy, we will go jogging this weekend, won't we?

The Father: As a matter of fact, I did not plan to go this weekend, but if you want, why not?

I was very pleased and excited to hear this. I was wondering if I would see the honeybee that had talked to me again.

When we arrived at the woods, I was even more excited. I could not wait to meet the honeybee again. I started jogging with my father. Soon we reached the place where I had first met the honeybee. I told my father that I wanted to look around a little bit. He accepted, but reminded me not to be back late. I ran quickly to our meeting place. My friend was already there waiting for me. It was obvious that he had been there for a while.

Omar: Hello! I am very happy to see you again!

30

The Honeybee: So am I! Welcóme! It is nice to see you too. I will keep my promise and show you the honeycomb today.

Omar: Great! You know what? I spent the whole week thinking about your amazing honeycombs? I can't wait to see them!

From a tree only a few steps away, an incredible buzzing could be heard. I would never have dared to go there if I had not had my friend with me. The little honeybee promised that nothing would happen to me, and I trusted him.

When we approached the tree trunk, I remembered that there was great order inside, despite the buzzing noise I was hearing. Honeybees are one of the most hard-working animals in the universe; they work without a moment's rest and produce the delicious honey that has so many uses for man. My little friend showed me the honeycomb cells; they were so regularly made that one could not help wondering how these tiny creatures could make such a perfect construction.

The cells I saw were made up of perfectly neat hexagons, or six-sided figures. In our maths class last week, I had asked my teacher some questions about hexagons. She had then briefly explained hexagons to me, but there were still some questions in my mind.

I asked my friend about the guidelines for constructing a hexagon honeycomb cell. He told me that the senior honeybee, who was the eldest bee, could give me the best answer. He then called over the senior bee, who answered my question:

Senior Bee: When we make a hexagonal cell, we pay special attention to the inside angles of the comb cells. We have to make each one 120 degrees. Besides, the tilt of the cells to the ground is also very important. If we take care of the other point and miss this one, then the cell will not be the proper shape and all the honey we store in the comb will spill out on to the ground.

Omar: To tell you the truth, that is quite difficult for me to understand, as I am not very familiar with the subject. How can honeybees make these calculations without any errors? How can you set each angle exactly at 120 degrees? And then you do not use any tools when building these combs. That reminds me of all the pages full of queer geometrical shapes I drew while trying to draw proper hexagons... I am even more amazed by you now!

Senior Bee: Don't be amazed at us; we do not do these things by ourselves! These are innate skills.

In other words, we are born with these skills. We do not receive any training or anything like that.

Omar: You show great wisdom! Everyone needs to learn the things you are doing. I would like to ask you a few things, if you will let me.

Senior Bee: Sure...

While constructing the cells, honeybees calculate the degrees of angles just like expert engineers. At the end, the comb that emerges is a wonder of engineering. There is no doubt that tiny bees cannot make these calculations by themselves. Like all other creatures in the universe, they act upon the inspiration of God.

Omar: Why do you make your combs in a hexagonal shape?

Senior Bee: I see. You want to know why we don't make them squares, triangles, pentagons or octagons, but hexagons... If we had made the honeycomb in another shape, there would be areas left unused in between the cells; in that way, we would be able to store less honey and would have to waste wax to patch the gaps. Actually, we could also store honey in squares or triangles but the hexagon is the shape with the shortest circumference. Despite having the same volume as other forms, we use less wax to make hexagonal cells than we would use to make triangles or squares. In other words, we can store the maximum amount of honey in hexagonal combs and use the minimum amount of wax.

I couldn't believe my ears! I was taking engineering lessons from a tiny, lovely honeybee... There were many other things I wanted to ask and learn. But it was getting late, so we left the senior honeybee and started to walk towards my father.

Omar: I have learned a lot from you and the other honeybees. Now I realise that before, I was completely unaware of the beauties which existed before my eyes! You have taught me that there is perfect order in the universe.

34

From now on, I hope I will be able to notice all this perfection. Thank you very much!

The Honeybee: Not at all, my little friend... Never forget that none of this perfection belongs to us! We only carry out what we are taught. Bye bye!

As I left the honeybee, I heard my father calling my name.

Honeybees collecting nectar from flowers to produce honey.

It was quite late. I hurried back to meet my father, but my mind was still set on my little friend! Just as I was getting into the car, I saw a butterfly. It had great colour harmony and symmetry in its wings. I decided to go to the school library the next day to do research on butterflies.

One could never count all the beauties created by God. I realised that there was much more to learn...